KEEP THE CHANGE, FRIEND. I'M FEELING GENEROUS TODAY.

BLASTED RAIN.

BY THE GODS, DON'T LET ME BE TOO LATE.

HOLD, MUSE. THIS IS NOT YOUR FIGHT.

PUT THAT AWAY, CHOOSER OF THE SLAIN, OR DO YOU INTEND TO USE IT?

ONLY IF YOU DARE TO MAKE ME, AVATAR OF "JUSTICE."

YOU CAUGHT ME ON A BAD DAY, LADY. A REALLY BAD DAY.

SO, YEAH. I DARE.

SO BE IT, MUSE.

KRAH-WANG!

I... I COULDN'T DO IT, EMMA.

CLATTER!

SHHH. IT'S OKAY, JULIANNA. IT'S OKAY. YOU'LL BE OKAY.

YES, SHE WILL, 10TH MUSE.

ALTHOUGH HER ANGER REMAINS, PERHAPS SHE CAN LEARN TO LIVE AGAIN AND TAKE SOLACE IN THE FACT THAT SHE IS STRONG. SHE DID NOT TAKE A LIFE THIS EVENING, EVEN ONE AS WORTHLESS AS HIS.

ARE YOU SATISFIED, FIEND?

WELL, THAT'S NOT CREEPY AT ALL.

C'MON, JULIANNA, LET'S GET YOU HOME.

CRISIS AVERTED, I GUESS. JULIANNA SEEMS... BETTER.

DISRESPECT! THAT'S WHAT IT IS! WHO DO YOU THINK YOU ARE, ANYWAY!

I HOPE THE EVENTS OF TONIGHT HELP HER HEAL. SHE CAME CLOSE TO BEING LOST.

I UNDERSTAND WHY THANATOS APPEARED. HE SENSED DEATH.

YOU CAN'T TAKE HER!

BUT... VALKYRIE'S MISSION IS DIFFERENT. SHE ESCORTS WARRIORS TO SALVATION AFTER THEY FALL IN BATTLE.

SHE'S MY DAUGHTER, TOO! I WON'T LET YOU!

WHAT ABOUT THIS NIGHT SUMMONED HER? IF SOMEONE IS GOING TO DIE, THEN...

I'LL DO YOU, HER, AND THEN ME, AND PROBLEM SOLVED, RIGHT?

TIDALWAVE
COMICS

Michael Frizell — Writer

Paulo Montes — Art

Benjamin Glibert — Letters

Alexandre Starling — Colors

Yonami — Cover

Darren G. Davis
Publisher

Maggie Jessup
Publicity

Susan Ferris
Entertainment Manager

Steven Diggs Jr.
Marketing Manager

CPSIA information can be obtained
at www.ICGtesting.com
Printed in the USA
LVHW061918230922
728951LV00008B/325

9 781956 841565